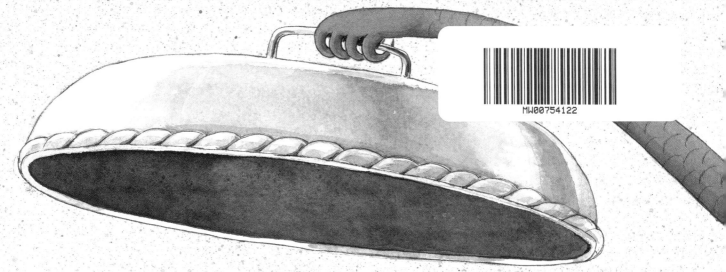

DRAGONS LOVE TACOS

by Adam Rubin
illustrated by Daniel Salmieri

SCHOLASTIC INC.

ISBN 978-0-545-60426-0

24   21 22/0

Printed in the U.S.A.   40

First Scholastic printing, September 2013

Designed by Jennifer Kelly
Text set in Zemke Hand ITC Std
The artwork was created with watercolor, gouache, and color pencil.

To my loving sister Bruce:
smart, beautiful, and full of laughter.
—AR

For Aaron, a wonderful friend.
Thank you for everything.
—DS

Hey, kid!

Did you know that dragons love tacos?

They love beef tacos and chicken tacos.

They love really big gigantic tacos and tiny little baby tacos as well.

Why do dragons love tacos?

Maybe it's the smell from the sizzling pan.

Maybe it's the crunch of the crispy tortillas.

Maybe it's a secret.

Either way, if you want to make friends with dragons, tacos are key.

Hey dragon, why do you guys love tacos so much?

But wait!

As much as dragons love tacos, they hate spicy salsa even more.

They hate spicy green salsa and spicy red salsa.

They hate spicy chunky salsa and spicy smooth salsa.

If the salsa is spicy at all, dragons can't stand it.

Why do dragons hate spicy salsa?
Well, just one drop of hot sauce
makes a dragon's ears smoke.

Just one single speck of hot pepper makes a dragon snort sparks.
Spicy salsa gives dragons the tummy troubles,
and when dragons get the tummy troubles—
oh boy . . .

If you want to make tacos for dragons, keep the toppings mild.

Tomatoes,

lettuce,

cheese,

these are all good toppings
for tacos for dragons.

Hey dragon, how do you feel about spicy taco toppings?

Dragons love parties. They like costume parties

and pool parties.

They like big gigantic parties with accordions

and tiny little parties with charades.

Why do dragons love parties? Maybe it's the conversation. Maybe it's the dancing. Maybe it's the comforting sound of a good friend's laughter.

The only thing dragons love more than parties or tacos, is taco parties (taco parties are parties with lots of tacos).

If you want to have some dragons over for a taco party, you'll need buckets of tacos. Pantloads of tacos. The best way to judge is to get a boat and fill the boat with tacos. That's about how many tacos dragons need for a taco party. After all, dragons love tacos.

Hey dragon, are you excited for the big taco party?

Just remember: Dragons hate spicy salsa.
Before you host your taco party with dragons,
get rid of all the spicy salsa. In fact, bury the spicy
salsa in the backyard so the dragons can't find it.

These dragons love your taco party! They love the music.
They love the decorations. They especially love the tacos.

Congratulations!

It's a good thing you got rid of all that spicy . . .

Wait a second—
what are those little green things in the salsa?
You didn't read the fine print?!

Dragons, listen to me: Do not eat those tacos.

Those little green specs in the salsa? Those are jalapeño peppers—they are super-spicy! I know you love tacos, dragons, but you are not gonna love those tacos.

DO NOT LET THOSE DRAGONS EAT THOSE TACOS!!!

Crunch, crunch, crunch...

Too late . . .

Why would dragons help you rebuild your house?

Maybe they're good Samaritans.

Maybe they feel bad for wrecking it.

Maybe they're just in it for the taco breaks.

After all, dragons love tacos.

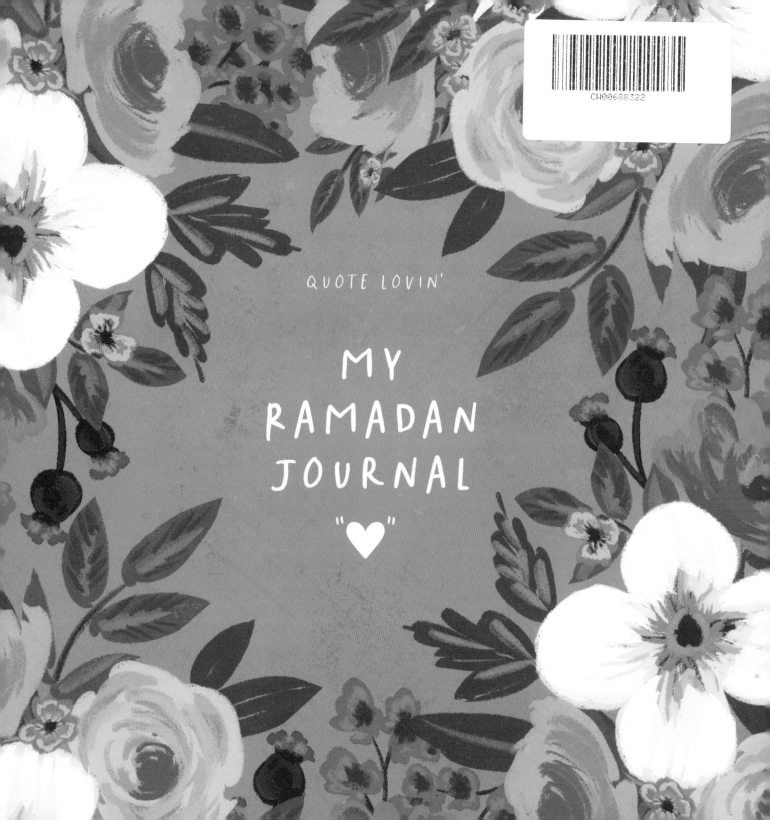

QUOTE LOVIN'

MY
RAMADAN
JOURNAL

"♥"

MAY ALLAH SWT
GRANT YOU A BLESSED RAMADAN.
AMEEN.

QUOTE LOVIN'

" "

RAMADAN OVERVIEW

1	2	3	4	5
6	7	8	9	10
11	12	13	14	15
16	17	18	19	20
21	22	23	24	25
26	27	28	29	30

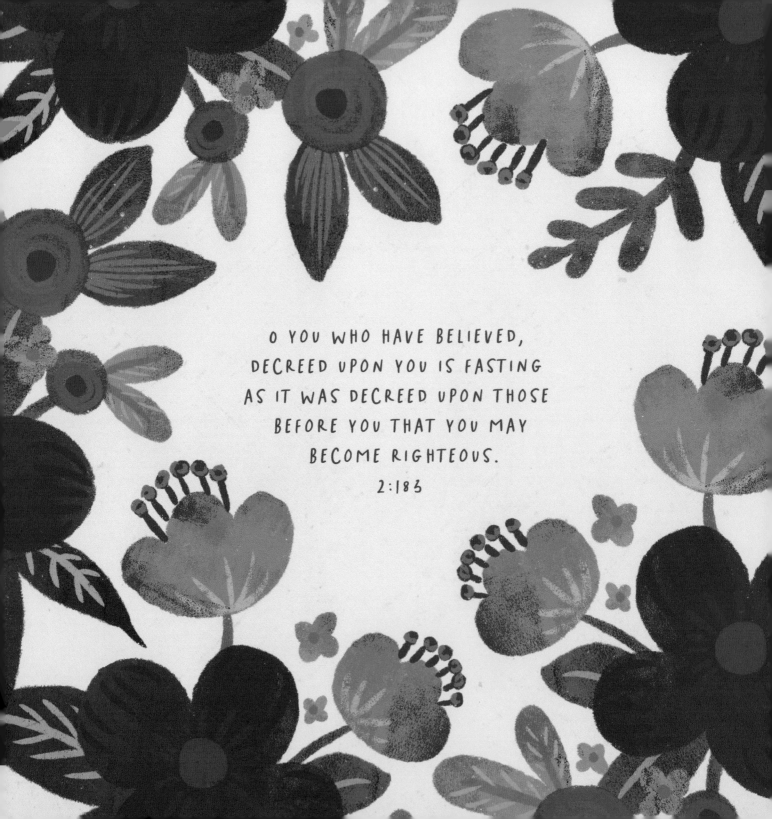

O YOU WHO HAVE BELIEVED,
DECREED UPON YOU IS FASTING
AS IT WAS DECREED UPON THOSE
BEFORE YOU THAT YOU MAY
BECOME RIGHTEOUS.

2:183

BISMILLAH

GOALS & INTENTIONS

NIGHT 1

..../..../....

TARAWIH:
(2 RAKATS EACH)

Ⓝ Ⓝ
Ⓝ Ⓝ
Ⓝ Ⓝ
Ⓝ Ⓝ
Ⓝ Ⓝ

TAHAJJUD:
(2 RAKATS EACH)

Ⓝ Ⓝ
Ⓝ Ⓝ

REMINDERS:

1).................................
2).................................
3).................................
4).................................

DU'AS:

"OUR LORD!
ACCEPT (THIS SERVICE) FROM US.
VERILY! YOU ARE
THE ALL-HEARER,
THE ALL-KNOWER."
2:127

ALLAH'S MESSENGER
(ﷺ) SAID,
"WHEN THE MONTH OF
RAMADAN STARTS,
THE GATES OF THE HEAVEN
ARE OPENED
AND THE GATES OF HELL
ARE CLOSED
AND THE DEVILS
ARE CHAINED."

SAHIH AL-BUKHARI 1899

BISMILLAH

DAY 1

..../..../....

FAJR
(S) (F)
2 RAKATS 2 RAKATS

DHUHR
(S) (F) (S) (N)
4 RAKATS 4 RAKATS 2 RAKATS 2 RAKATS

ASR
(S) (F)
4 RAKATS 4 RAKATS

MAGRIB
(F) (S) (N)
6 RAKATS 2 RAKATS 2 RAKATS

ISHA
(S) (F) (S) (N) (W) (N)
4 RAKATS 4 RAKATS 2 RAKATS 2 RAKATS 6 RAKATS 2 RAKATS

☐ FASTED
☐ CHARITY
☐ ....
☐ ....

THOUGHTS & REFLECTIONS

NIGHT 2
TARAWIH:
(2 RAKATS EACH)

(N) (N)
(N) (N)
(N) (N)
(N) (N)
(N) (N)

TAHAJJUD:
(2 RAKATS EACH)

(N) (N)
(N) (N)

REMINDERS:
1) ....
2) ....
3) ....
4) ....

DU'AS:

OUR LORD!
GRANT US GOOD IN THIS WORLD
AND GOOD IN THE LIFE TO COME
(2:201)

BISMILLAH

FAJR
(S) (F)
2 RAKATS 2 RAKATS

DHUHR
(S) (F) (S) (N)
4 RAKATS 4 RAKATS 2 RAKATS 2 RAKATS

ASR
(S) (F)
4 RAKATS 4 RAKATS

MAGRIB
(F) (S) (N)
6 RAKATS 2 RAKATS 2 RAKATS

ISHA
(S) (F) (S) (N) (W) (N)
4 RAKATS 4 RAKATS 2 RAKATS 2 RAKATS 6 RAKATS 2 RAKATS

DAY 2

..... / ..... / .....

☐ FASTED
☐ CHARITY
☐ ....
☐ ....

NIGHT 3
TARAWIH:
(2 RAKATS EACH)

(N) (N)
(N) (N)
(N) (N)
(N) (N)
(N) (N)

TAHAJJUD:
(2 RAKATS EACH)

(N) (N)
(N) (N)

THOUGHTS & REFLECTIONS

REMINDERS:
1) ....
2) ....
3) ....
4) ....

DU'AS:
OUR LORD!
TAKE US NOT TO TASK
IF WE FORGET OR FALL
INTO ERROR. (2:286)

AND
MY MERCY
ENCOMPASSES
EVERYTHING

7:156

BISMILLAH

DAY 3

..../..../....

FAJR
(S) 2 RAKATS (F) 2 RAKATS

DHUHR
(S) 4 RAKATS (F) 4 RAKATS (S) 2 RAKATS (N) 2 RAKATS

ASR
(S) 4 RAKATS (F) 4 RAKATS

MAGRIB
(F) 6 RAKATS (S) 2 RAKATS (N) 2 RAKATS

ISHA
(S) 4 RAKATS (F) 4 RAKATS (S) 2 RAKATS (N) 2 RAKATS (W) 6 RAKATS (N) 2 RAKATS

THOUGHTS & REFLECTIONS

- [ ] FASTED
- [ ] CHARITY
- [ ] ....
- [ ] ....

NIGHT 4
TARAWIH:
(2 RAKATS EACH)

(N) (N)
(N) (N)
(N) (N)
(N) (N)
(N) (N)

TAHAJJUD:
(2 RAKATS EACH)

(N) (N)
(N) (N)

REMINDERS:

1) ....
2) ....
3) ....
4) ....

DU'AS:

OUR LORD!
LAY NOT UPON US SUCH A BURDEN
AS YOU DID LAY UPON THOSE
BEFORE US. (2:286)

GARDENS BENEATH WHICH RIVERS FLOW.

61:12

BISMILLAH

DAY 4
..... / ..... / .....

FAJR
(S) (F)
2 RAKATS 2 RAKATS

DHUHR
(S) (F) (S) (N)
4 RAKATS 4 RAKATS 2 RAKATS 2 RAKATS

ASR
(S) (F)
4 RAKATS 4 RAKATS

MAGRIB
(F) (S) (N)
6 RAKATS 2 RAKATS 2 RAKATS

ISHA
(S) (F) (S) (N) (W) (N)
4 RAKATS 4 RAKATS 2 RAKATS 2 RAKATS 6 RAKATS 2 RAKATS

THOUGHTS & REFLECTIONS

REMINDERS:
1) ....
2) ....
3) ....
4) ....

DU'AS:
OUR LORD! IMPOSE NOT ON US THAT WHICH
WE HAVE NOT THE STRENGTH TO BEAR,
GRANT US FORGIVENESS AND HAVE MERCY ON US.
YOU ARE OUR PROTECTOR.
HELP US AGAINST THOSE
WHO DENY THE TRUTH. (2:286)

☐ FASTED
☐ CHARITY
☐ ....
☐ ....

NIGHT 5
TARAWIH:
(2 RAKATS EACH)

(N) (N)
(N) (N)
(N) (N)
(N) (N)
(N) (N)

TAHAJJUD:
(2 RAKATS EACH)

(N) (N)
(N) (N)

BISMILLAH

DAY
5

.... / .... / ....

FAJR
(S) (F)
2 RAKATS 2 RAKATS
🤲 📿 🕋

DHUHR
(S) (F) (S) (N)
4 RAKATS 4 RAKATS 2 RAKATS 2 RAKATS
🤲 📿 🕋

ASR
(S) (F)
4 RAKATS 4 RAKATS
🤲 📿 🕋

MAGRIB
(F) (S) (N)
6 RAKATS 2 RAKATS 2 RAKATS
🤲 📿 🕋

ISHA
(S) (F) (S) (N) (W) (N)
4 RAKATS 4 RAKATS 2 RAKATS 2 RAKATS 6 RAKATS 2 RAKATS
🤲 📿 🕋

☐ FASTED
☐ CHARITY
☐ ....
☐ ....

THOUGHTS & REFLECTIONS

NIGHT 6
TARAWIH:
(2 RAKATS EACH)

(N) (N)
(N) (N)
(N) (N)
(N) (N)
(N) (N)

TAHAJJUD:
(2 RAKATS EACH)

(N) (N)
(N) (N)

REMINDERS:
1) ....
2) ....
3) ....
4) ....

DU'AS:
OUR LORD! LET NOT OUR HEARTS DEVIATE
FROM THE TRUTH AFTER YOU HAVE GUIDED US,
AND BESTOW UPON US MERCY FROM YOUR GRACE.
VERILY YOU ARE THE GIVER
OF BOUNTIES WITHOUT MEASURE. (3:8)

ALLAH
IS THE CREATOR
OF ALL
THINGS.

39:62

BISMILLAH

FAJR
(S) (F)
2 RAKATS 2 RAKATS

DHUHR
(S) (F) (S) (N)
4 RAKATS 4 RAKATS 2 RAKATS 2 RAKATS

ASR
(S) (F)
4 RAKATS 4 RAKATS

MAGRIB
(F) (S) (N)
6 RAKATS 2 RAKATS 2 RAKATS

ISHA
(S) (F) (S) (N) (W) (N)
4 RAKATS 4 RAKATS 2 RAKATS 2 RAKATS 6 RAKATS 2 RAKATS

THOUGHTS & REFLECTIONS

REMINDERS:
1) ....
2) ....
3) ....
4) ....

DU'AS:
OUR LORD!
FORGIVE US OUR SINS
AND THE LACK OF MODERATION IN OUR DOINGS,
AND MAKE FIRM OUR STEPS
AND SUCCOUR US AGAINST
THOSE WHO DENY THE TRUTH. (3:147)

DAY 6

..... / ..... / .....

☐ FASTED
☐ CHARITY
☐ ....
☐ ....

NIGHT 7
TARAWIH:
(2 RAKATS EACH)

(N) (N)
(N) (N)
(N) (N)
(N) (N)
(N) (N)

TAHAJJUD:
(2 RAKATS EACH)

(N) (N)
(N) (N)

SO REMEMBER
ME:
I WILL REMEMBER
YOU.

2:152

BISMILLAH

FAJR
(S) (F)
2 RAKATS 2 RAKATS

DHUHR
(S) (F) (S) (N)
4 RAKATS 4 RAKATS 2 RAKATS 2 RAKATS

ASR
(S) (F)
4 RAKATS 4 RAKATS

MAGRIB
(F) (S) (N)
6 RAKATS 2 RAKATS 2 RAKATS

ISHA
(S) (F) (S) (N) (W) (N)
4 RAKATS 4 RAKATS 2 RAKATS 2 RAKATS 6 RAKATS 2 RAKATS

THOUGHTS & REFLECTIONS

☐ FASTED
☐ CHARITY
☐ ....
☐ ....

NIGHT 8
TARAWIH:
(2 RAKATS EACH)

(N) (N)
(N) (N)
(N) (N)
(N) (N)
(N) (N)

TAHAJJUD:
(2 RAKATS EACH)

(N) (N)
(N) (N)

REMINDERS:
1) ....
2) ....
3) ....
4) ....

DU'AS:
OUR LORD!
FORGIVE US OUR SINS
AND EFFACE OUR BAD DEEDS
AND TAKE OUR SOULS
IN THE COMPANY
OF THE RIGHTEOUS. (3:193)

BISMILLAH

DAY
8

..... / ..... / .....

FAJR
(S) (F)
2 RAKATS 2 RAKATS

DHUHR
(S) (F) (S) (N)
4 RAKATS 4 RAKATS 2 RAKATS 2 RAKATS

ASR
(S) (F)
4 RAKATS 4 RAKATS

MAGRIB
(F) (S) (N)
3 RAKATS 2 RAKATS 2 RAKATS

ISHA
(S) (F) (S) (N) (W) (N)
4 RAKATS 4 RAKATS 2 RAKATS 2 RAKATS 3 RAKATS 2 RAKATS

THOUGHTS & REFLECTIONS

- [ ] FASTED
- [ ] CHARITY
- [ ] ....
- [ ] ....

NIGHT 9
TARAWIH:
(2 RAKATS EACH)

(N) (N)
(N) (N)
(N) (N)
(N) (N)
(N) (N)

REMINDERS:

1) ....
2) ....
3) ....
4) ....

DU'AS:

OUR LORD! AND GRANT US
THAT WHICH YOU HAVE PROMISED TO US
BY YOUR MESSENGERS
AND SAVE US FROM SHAME
ON THE DAY OF JUDGEMENT.
VERILY YOU NEVER FAIL
TO FULFILL YOUR PROMISE. (3:194)

TAHAJJUD:
(2 RAKATS EACH)

(N) (N)
(N) (N)

SO WHICH OF THE FAVOURS OF YOUR LORD WOULD YOU DENY? 55:13

BISMILLAH

DAY
9
.... / .... / ....

FAJR
(S) (F)
2 RAKATS 2 RAKATS

DHUHR
(S) (F) (S) (N)
4 RAKATS 4 RAKATS 2 RAKATS 2 RAKATS

ASR
(S) (F)
4 RAKATS 4 RAKATS

MAGRIB
(F) (S) (N)
6 RAKATS 2 RAKATS 2 RAKATS

ISHA
(S) (F) (S) (N) (W) (N)
4 RAKATS 4 RAKATS 2 RAKATS 2 RAKATS 6 RAKATS 2 RAKATS

☐ FASTED
☐ CHARITY
☐ ....
☐ ....

THOUGHTS & REFLECTIONS

NIGHT 10
TARAWIH:
(2 RAKATS EACH)

(N) (N)
(N) (N)
(N) (N)
(N) (N)
(N) (N)

REMINDERS:
1) ....
2) ....
3) ....
4) ....

DU'AS:
OUR LORD!
WE HAVE SINNED AGAINST OURSELVES,
AND UNLESS YOU GRANT US FORGIVENESS
AND BESTOW YOUR MERCY UPON US,
WE SHALL MOST CERTAINLY BE LOST! (7:23)

TAHAJJUD:
(2 RAKATS EACH)

(N) (N)
(N) (N)

BISMILLAH

FAJR
(S) (F)
2 RAKATS 2 RAKATS

DHUHR
(S) (F) (S) (N)
4 RAKATS 4 RAKATS 2 RAKATS 2 RAKATS

ASR
(S) (F)
4 RAKATS 4 RAKATS

MAGRIB
(F) (S) (N)
6 RAKATS 2 RAKATS 2 RAKATS

ISHA
(S) (F) (S) (N) (W) (N)
4 RAKATS 4 RAKATS 2 RAKATS 2 RAKATS 6 RAKATS 2 RAKATS

DAY 10
..../..../....

- [ ] FASTED
- [ ] CHARITY
- [ ] ....
- [ ] ....

NIGHT 11
TARAWIH:
(2 RAKATS EACH)

THOUGHTS & REFLECTIONS

TAHAJJUD:
(2 RAKATS EACH)

REMINDERS:
1)..
2)..
3)..
4)..

DU'AS:

OUR LORD!
BESTOW ON US MERCY
FROM YOUR PRESENCE
AND DISPOSE OF OUR AFFAIRS FOR US
IN THE RIGHT WAY. (18:10)

LOOK AT ITS FRUIT
WHEN IT BEARS FRUIT,
AND AT ITS RIPENING. SURELY,
IN ALL THIS THERE ARE SIGNS
FOR THE PEOPLE
WHO BELIEVE.
6:99

BISMILLAH

FAJR
(S) (F)
2 RAKATS 2 RAKATS

DHUHR
(S) (F) (S) (N)
4 RAKATS 4 RAKATS 2 RAKATS 2 RAKATS

ASR
(S) (F)
4 RAKATS 4 RAKATS

MAGRIB
(F) (S) (N)
6 RAKATS 2 RAKATS 2 RAKATS

ISHA
(S) (F) (S) (N) (W) (N)
4 RAKATS 4 RAKATS 2 RAKATS 2 RAKATS 6 RAKATS 2 RAKATS

DAY
11
.... / .... / ....

☐ FASTED
☐ CHARITY
☐ ....
☐ ....

NIGHT 12
TARAWIH:
(2 RAKATS EACH)

THOUGHTS & REFLECTIONS

REMINDERS:
1) ....
2) ....
3) ....
4) ....

DU'AS:
OUR LORD!
GRANT THAT OUR SPOUSES
AND OUR OFFSPRING
BE A COMFORT TO OUR EYES,
AND GIVE US THE GRACE TO LEAD THOSE
WHO ARE CONSCIOUS OF YOU. (25:74)

TAHAJJUD:
(2 RAKATS EACH)

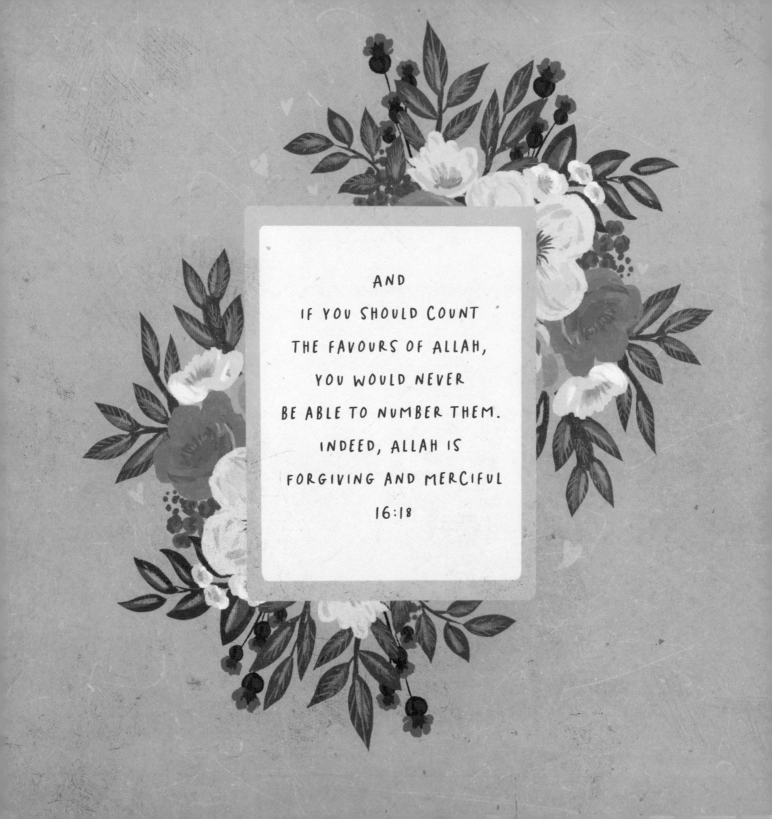

AND
IF YOU SHOULD COUNT
THE FAVOURS OF ALLAH,
YOU WOULD NEVER
BE ABLE TO NUMBER THEM.
INDEED, ALLAH IS
FORGIVING AND MERCIFUL

16:18

BISMILLAH

FAJR
(S) (F)
2 RAKATS   2 RAKATS

DHUHR
(S) (F) (S) (N)
4 RAKATS   4 RAKATS   2 RAKATS   2 RAKATS

ASR
(S) (F)
4 RAKATS   4 RAKATS

MAGRIB
(F) (S) (N)
6 RAKATS   2 RAKATS   2 RAKATS

ISHA
(S) (F) (S) (N) (W) (N)
4 RAKATS   4 RAKATS   2 RAKATS   2 RAKATS   6 RAKATS   2 RAKATS

DAY 12
..../..../....

- [ ] FASTED
- [ ] CHARITY
- [ ] ....
- [ ] ....

THOUGHTS & REFLECTIONS

NIGHT 13

TARAWIH:
(2 RAKATS EACH)

(N) (N)
(N) (N)
(N) (N)
(N) (N)
(N) (N)

TAHAJJUD:
(2 RAKATS EACH)

(N) (N)
(N) (N)

REMINDERS:
1) ....
2) ....
3) ....
4) ....

DU'AS:
OUR LORD!
IN YOU WE HAVE PLACED OUR TRUST,
AND TO YOU DO WE TURN IN REPENTANCE,
FOR UNTO YOU IS THE END
OF ALL JOURNEYS. (60:4)

SPEND
IN THE CAUSE OF ALLAH
AND DO NOT LET YOUR OWN HANDS
THROW YOU INTO DESTRUCTION
BY WITHHOLDING .
AND DO GOOD,
FOR ALLAH CERTAINLY LOVES
THE GOOD-DOERS.

2:195

BISMILLAH

FAJR
(S) (F)
2 RAKATS 2 RAKATS
🙌 📿 📖

DHUHR
(S) (F) (S) (N)
4 RAKATS 4 RAKATS 2 RAKATS 2 RAKATS
🙌 📿 📖

ASR
(S) (F)
4 RAKATS 4 RAKATS
🙌 📿 📖

MAGRIB
(F) (S) (N)
3 RAKATS 2 RAKATS 2 RAKATS
🙌 📿 📖

ISHA
(S) (F) (S) (N) (W) (N)
4 RAKATS 4 RAKATS 2 RAKATS 2 RAKATS 3 RAKATS 2 RAKATS
🙌 📿 📖

THOUGHTS & REFLECTIONS

☐ FASTED
☐ CHARITY
☐ ....
☐ ....

NIGHT 14
TARAWIH:
(2 RAKATS EACH)

(N) (N)
(N) (N)
(N) (N)
(N) (N)
(N) (N)

TAHAJJUD:
(2 RAKATS EACH)

(N) (N)
(N) (N)

REMINDERS:
1).................................
2).................................
3).................................
4).................................

DU'AS:

OUR LORD!
PERFECT OUR LIGHT FOR US
AND FORGIVE US OUR SINS,
FOR VERILY YOU HAVE POWER
OVER ALL THINGS. (66:8)

IT IS HE WHO HAS MADE THE EARTH

A RESTING PLACE FOR YOU. 2:22

BISMILLAH

DAY 14
.... / .... / ....

FAJR
(S) (F)
2 RAKATS 2 RAKATS

DHUHR
(S) (F) (S) (N)
4 RAKATS 4 RAKATS 2 RAKATS 2 RAKATS

ASR
(S) (F)
4 RAKATS 4 RAKATS

MAGRIB
(F) (S) (N)
6 RAKATS 2 RAKATS 2 RAKATS

ISHA
(S) (F) (S) (N) (W) (N)
4 RAKATS 4 RAKATS 2 RAKATS 2 RAKATS 6 RAKATS 2 RAKATS

THOUGHTS & REFLECTIONS

- [ ] FASTED
- [ ] CHARITY
- [ ] ....
- [ ] ....

NIGHT 15

TARAWIH:
(2 RAKATS EACH)

(N) (N)
(N) (N)
(N) (N)
(N) (N)
(N) (N)

TAHAJJUD:
(2 RAKATS EACH)

(N) (N)
(N) (N)

REMINDERS:
1) ....
2) ....
3) ....
4) ....

DU'AS:
"O ALLAH,
I HOPE FOR YOUR MERCY.
DO NOT LEAVE ME TO MYSELF
EVEN FOR THE BLINKING OF AN EYE
(I.E. A MOMENT).
CORRECT ALL OF MY AFFAIRS FOR ME.
THERE IS NONE WORTHY
OF WORSHIP BUT YOU." (ABU DAWUD)

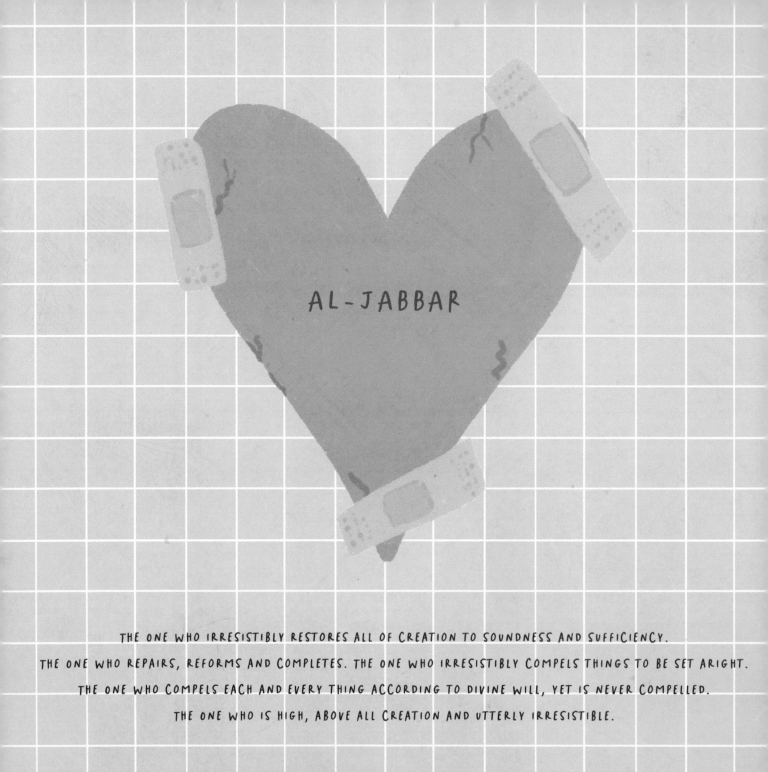

AL-JABBAR

THE ONE WHO IRRESISTIBLY RESTORES ALL OF CREATION TO SOUNDNESS AND SUFFICIENCY.
THE ONE WHO REPAIRS, REFORMS AND COMPLETES. THE ONE WHO IRRESISTIBLY COMPELS THINGS TO BE SET ARIGHT.
THE ONE WHO COMPELS EACH AND EVERY THING ACCORDING TO DIVINE WILL, YET IS NEVER COMPELLED.
THE ONE WHO IS HIGH, ABOVE ALL CREATION AND UTTERLY IRRESISTIBLE.

BISMILLAH

FAJR
(S) (F)
2 RAKATS 2 RAKATS

DHUHR
(S) (F) (S) (N)
4 RAKATS 4 RAKATS 2 RAKATS 2 RAKATS

ASR
(S) (F)
4 RAKATS 4 RAKATS

MAGRIB
(F) (S) (N)
6 RAKATS 2 RAKATS 2 RAKATS

ISHA
(S) (F) (S) (N) (W) (N)
4 RAKATS 4 RAKATS 2 RAKATS 2 RAKATS 6 RAKATS 2 RAKATS

DAY 15
..../..../....

- [ ] FASTED
- [ ] CHARITY
- [ ] ....
- [ ] ....

NIGHT 16
TARAWIH:
(2 RAKATS EACH)

(N)(N)
(N)(N)
(N)(N)
(N)(N)
(N)(N)

TAHAJJUD:
(2 RAKATS EACH)

(N)(N)
(N)(N)

THOUGHTS & REFLECTIONS

REMINDERS:
1) ....
2) ....
3) ....
4) ....

DU'AS:
"O ALLAH,
I HAVE FASTED FOR YOU
AND FROM THE SUSTENANCE
GIVEN BY YOU,
I BREAK THE FAST".
(ABU DAWOOD)

BISMILLAH

DAY 16
.... / .... / ....

FAJR
(S) (F)
2 RAKATS 2 RAKATS

DHUHR
(S) (F) (S) (N)
4 RAKATS 4 RAKATS 2 RAKATS 2 RAKATS

ASR
(S) (F)
4 RAKATS 4 RAKATS

MAGRIB
(F) (S) (N)
6 RAKATS 2 RAKATS 2 RAKATS

ISHA
(S) (F) (S) (N) (W) (N)
4 RAKATS 4 RAKATS 2 RAKATS 2 RAKATS 6 RAKATS 2 RAKATS

☐ FASTED
☐ CHARITY
☐ ....
☐ ....

THOUGHTS & REFLECTIONS

NIGHT 17
TARAWIH:
(2 RAKATS EACH)

(N) (N)
(N) (N)
(N) (N)
(N) (N)
(N) (N)

TAHAJJUD:
(2 RAKATS EACH)

(N) (N)
(N) (N)

REMINDERS:
1) ....
2) ....
3) ....
4) ....

DU'AS:
"THE THIRST HAS QUENCHED
AND LEFT WETNESS
AND WITH THE WILL OF ALLAH,
REWARD IS PROVEN (CERTAIN)"
ABU DAWOOD

SUFFICIENT FOR US IS ALLAH,
AND [HE IS] THE BEST DISPOSER OF AFFAIRS.
3:173

BISMILLAH

FAJR
(S) (F)
2 RAKATS 2 RAKATS

DHUHR
(S) (F) (S) (N)
4 RAKATS 4 RAKATS 2 RAKATS 2 RAKATS

ASR
(S) (F)
4 RAKATS 4 RAKATS

MAGRIB
(F) (S) (N)
6 RAKATS 2 RAKATS 2 RAKATS

ISHA
(S) (F) (S) (N) (W) (N)
4 RAKATS 4 RAKATS 2 RAKATS 2 RAKATS 6 RAKATS 2 RAKATS

DAY 17
..../..../....

- [ ] FASTED
- [ ] CHARITY
- [ ] ....
- [ ] ....

THOUGHTS & REFLECTIONS

NIGHT 18
TARAWIH:
(2 RAKATS EACH)

TAHAJJUD:
(2 RAKATS EACH)

REMINDERS:
1) ....
2) ....
3) ....
4) ....

DU'AS:
OUR LORD, AND MAKE US MUSLIMS
[IN SUBMISSION] TO YOU
AND FROM OUR DESCENDANTS
A MUSLIM NATION [IN SUBMISSION] TO YOU.
AND SHOW US OUR RITES
AND ACCEPT OUR REPENTANCE
. INDEED, YOU ARE THE ACCEPTING
OF REPENTANCE, THE MERCIFUL.
2:128

In Jannah, you will find
every kind of fruit!

BISMILLAH

DAY 18

..... / ..... / .....

FAJR
(S) (F)
2 RAKATS 2 RAKATS

DHUHR
(S) (F) (S) (N)
4 RAKATS 4 RAKATS 2 RAKATS 2 RAKATS

ASR
(S) (F)
4 RAKATS 4 RAKATS

MAGRIB
(F) (S) (N)
6 RAKATS 2 RAKATS 2 RAKATS

ISHA
(S) (F) (S) (N) (W) (N)
4 RAKATS 4 RAKATS 2 RAKATS 2 RAKATS 6 RAKATS 2 RAKATS

THOUGHTS & REFLECTIONS

☐ FASTED
☐ CHARITY
☐ ....
☐ ....

NIGHT 19

TARAWIH:
(2 RAKATS EACH)

(N) (N)
(N) (N)
(N) (N)
(N) (N)
(N) (N)

TAHAJJUD:
(2 RAKATS EACH)

(N) (N)
(N) (N)

REMINDERS:
1) ....
2) ....
3) ....
4) ....

DU'AS:

OUR LORD,
WE HAVE BELIEVED,
SO REGISTER US
AMONG THE WITNESSES..

5:80

AND
ALLAH IS
THE BEST PROVIDER.
62: 11

BISMILLAH

FAJR
(S) (F)
2 RAKATS 2 RAKATS

DHUHR
(S) (F) (S) (N)
4 RAKATS 4 RAKATS 2 RAKATS 2 RAKATS

ASR
(S) (F)
4 RAKATS 4 RAKATS

MAGRIB
(F) (S) (N)
6 RAKATS 2 RAKATS 2 RAKATS

ISHA
(S) (F) (S) (N) (W) (N)
4 RAKATS 4 RAKATS 2 RAKATS 2 RAKATS 6 RAKATS 2 RAKATS

DAY 19
..... / ..... / .....

THOUGHTS & REFLECTIONS

- [ ] FASTED
- [ ] CHARITY
- [ ] ....
- [ ] ....

NIGHT 20
TARAWIH:
(2 RAKATS EACH)

(N) (N)
(N) (N)
(N) (N)
(N) (N)
(N) (N)

TAHAJJUD:
(2 RAKATS EACH)

(N) (N)
(N) (N)

REMINDERS:
1) ....
2) ....
3) ....
4) ....

DU'AS:
OUR LORD,
INDEED YOU KNOW WHAT WE CONCEAL
AND WHAT WE DECLARE,
AND NOTHING IS HIDDEN
FROM ALLAH ON THE EARTH
OR IN THE HEAVEN.

14:38

BISMILLAH

DAY 20
.... / .... / ....

FAJR
(S) (F)
2 RAKATS 2 RAKATS

DHUHR
(S) (F) (S) (N)
4 RAKATS 4 RAKATS 2 RAKATS 2 RAKATS

ASR
(S) (F)
4 RAKATS 4 RAKATS

MAGRIB
(F) (S) (N)
6 RAKATS 2 RAKATS 2 RAKATS

ISHA
(S) (F) (S) (N) (W) (N)
4 RAKATS 4 RAKATS 2 RAKATS 2 RAKATS 6 RAKATS 2 RAKATS

THOUGHTS & REFLECTIONS

REMINDERS:
1) ....
2) ....
3) ....
4) ....

DU'AS:
OUR LORD,
FORGIVE ME AND MY PARENTS
AND THE BELIEVERS THE DAY
THE ACCOUNT IS ESTABLISHED.

14:41

☐ FASTED
☐ CHARITY
☐ ....
☐ ....

NIGHT 21
TARAWIH:
(2 RAKATS EACH)

TAHAJJUD:
(2 RAKATS EACH)

BISMILLAH

DAY 21

..../..../....

FAJR
(S) (F)
2 RAKATS · 2 RAKATS
🤲 📿 📖

DHUHR
(S) (F) (S) (N)
4 RAKATS · 4 RAKATS · 2 RAKATS · 2 RAKATS
🤲 📿 📖

ASR
(S) (F)
4 RAKATS · 4 RAKATS

MAGRIB
(F) (S) (N)
6 RAKATS · 2 RAKATS · 2 RAKATS
🤲 📿 📖

ISHA
(S) (F) (S) (N) (W) (N)
4 RAKATS · 4 RAKATS · 2 RAKATS · 2 RAKATS · 6 RAKATS · 2 RAKATS
🤲 📿 📖

☐ FASTED
☐ CHARITY
☐ ....
☐ ....

THOUGHTS & REFLECTIONS

NIGHT 22

TARAWIH:
(2 RAKATS EACH)

(N) (N)
(N) (N)
(N) (N)
(N) (N)
(N) (N)

TAHAJJUD:
(2 RAKATS EACH)

(N) (N)
(N) (N)

REMINDERS:
1) ....
2) ....
3) ....
4) ....

DU'AS:
MY LORD,
GRANT PARDON
AND HAVE MERCY,
FOR YOU ARE THE BEST
OF ALL THE MERCIFUL
23:118

AND SAY
"MY LORD,
INCREASE
ME IN
KNOWLEDGE"
20:114

BISMILLAH

FAJR
(S) (F)
2 RAKATS   2 RAKATS

DHUHR
(S) (F) (S) (N)
4 RAKATS   4 RAKATS   2 RAKATS   2 RAKATS

ASR
(S) (F)
4 RAKATS   4 RAKATS

MAGRIB
(F) (S) (N)
6 RAKATS   2 RAKATS   2 RAKATS

ISHA
(S) (F) (S) (N) (W) (N)
4 RAKATS   4 RAKATS   2 RAKATS   2 RAKATS   6 RAKATS   2 RAKATS

DAY 22

.... / .... / ....

☐ FASTED
☐ CHARITY
☐ ....
☐ ....

NIGHT 23

TARAWIH:
(2 RAKATS EACH)

(N) (N)
(N) (N)
(N) (N)
(N) (N)
(N) (N)

TAHAJJUD:
(2 RAKATS EACH)

(N) (N)
(N) (N)

THOUGHTS & REFLECTIONS

REMINDERS:
1) ....
2) ....
3) ....
4) ....

DU'AS:

MY LORD,
I AM IN NEED OF WHATEVER GOOD
YOU SEND DOWN TO ME.

28:24

IT IS HE WHO MADE THE SUN TO BE A SHINING GLORY

AND THE MOON TO BE A LIGHT OF BEAUTY

10:5

BISMILLAH

DAY 23

..../..../....

FAJR
(S) (F)
2 RAKATS 2 RAKATS
🤲 📿 📖

DHUHR
(S) (F) (S) (N)
4 RAKATS 4 RAKATS 2 RAKATS 2 RAKATS
🤲 📿 📖

ASR
(S) (F)
4 RAKATS 4 RAKATS
🤲 📿 📖

MAGRIB
(F) (S) (N)
6 RAKATS 2 RAKATS 2 RAKATS
🤲 📿 📖

ISHA
(S) (F) (S) (N) (W) (N)
4 RAKATS 4 RAKATS 2 RAKATS 2 RAKATS 6 RAKATS 2 RAKATS
🤲 📿 📖

THOUGHTS & REFLECTIONS

☐ FASTED
☐ CHARITY
☐ ....
☐ ....

NIGHT 24

TARAWIH:
(2 RAKATS EACH)

(N) (N)
(N) (N)
(N) (N)
(N) (N)
(N) (N)

TAHAJJUD:
(2 RAKATS EACH)

(N) (N)
(N) (N)

REMINDERS:
1) ....
2) ....
3) ....
4) ....

DU'AS:
OUR LORD, AND ADMIT THEM TO GARDENS
OF PERPETUAL RESIDENCE
WHICH YOU HAVE PROMISED THEM
AND WHOEVER WAS RIGHTEOUS AMONG THEIR FATHERS,
THEIR SPOUSES AND THEIR OFFSPRING.
INDEED, IT IS YOU WHO IS THE EXALTED
IN MIGHT, THE WISE.

40:8

INDEED,
THE FIRST HOUSE [OF WORSHIP] ESTABLISHED FOR MANKIND
WAS THAT AT MAKKAH — BLESSED AND A GUIDANCE
FOR THE WORLDS.
3:96

BISMILLAH

DAY 24

..... / ..... / .....

FAJR
(S) (F)
2 RAKATS   2 RAKATS

DHUHR
(S) (F) (S) (N)
4 RAKATS 4 RAKATS 2 RAKATS 2 RAKATS

ASR
(S) (F)
4 RAKATS   4 RAKATS

MAGRIB
(F) (S) (N)
6 RAKATS 2 RAKATS 2 RAKATS

ISHA
(S) (F) (S) (N) (W) (N)
4 RAKATS 4 RAKATS 2 RAKATS 2 RAKATS 6 RAKATS 2 RAKATS

THOUGHTS & REFLECTIONS

- [ ] FASTED
- [ ] CHARITY
- [ ] ....
- [ ] ....

NIGHT 25

TARAWIH:
(2 RAKATS EACH)

TAHAJJUD:
(2 RAKATS EACH)

REMINDERS:

1) ....
2) ....
3) ....
4) ....

DU'AS:

MY LORD, ENABLE ME TO BE GRATEFUL
FOR YOUR FAVOR WHICH YOU HAVE BESTOWED UPON ME
AND UPON MY PARENTS AND TO WORK RIGHTEOUSNESS
OF WHICH YOU WILL APPROVE
AND MAKE RIGHTEOUS FOR ME MY OFFSPRING.
INDEED, I HAVE REPENTED TO YOU,
AND INDEED, I AM OF THE MUSLIMS.

46:15

BISMILLAH

DAY 25

..... / ..... / .....

FAJR
(S) (F)
2 RAKATS 2 RAKATS

DHUHR
(S) (F) (S) (N)
4 RAKATS 4 RAKATS 2 RAKATS 2 RAKATS

ASR
(S) (F)
4 RAKATS 4 RAKATS

MAGRIB
(F) (S) (N)
6 RAKATS 2 RAKATS 2 RAKATS

ISHA
(S) (F) (S) (N) (W) (N)
4 RAKATS 4 RAKATS 2 RAKATS 2 RAKATS 6 RAKATS 2 RAKATS

THOUGHTS & REFLECTIONS

☐ FASTED
☐ CHARITY
☐ ....
☐ ....

NIGHT 26

TARAWIH:
(2 RAKATS EACH)

TAHAJJUD:
(2 RAKATS EACH)

REMINDERS:
1) ....
2) ....
3) ....
4) ....

DU'AS:
MY LORD,
HAVE MERCY UPON THEM (PARENTS)
AS THEY BROUGHT ME UP
[WHEN I WAS] SMALL.
17:24

"WE HAVE INDEED
REVEALED THIS IN THE 'NIGHT OF POWER'.
AND WHAT WILL EXPLAIN TO YOU WHAT THE NIGHT OF POWER IS?
THE NIGHT OF POWER IS BETTER THAN A THOUSAND MONTHS.
THEREIN COME DOWN THE ANGELS AND THE SPIRIT BY ALLAH'S PERMISSION,
ON EVERY ERRAND.
"PEACE!...THIS UNTIL THE RISE OF MORN!"

SURAH AL-QADR 97: 1-5

BISMILLAH

DAY 26

..../..../....

FAJR
(S) (F)
2 RAKATS 2 RAKATS

DHUHR
(S) (F) (S) (N)
4 RAKATS 4 RAKATS 2 RAKATS 2 RAKATS

ASR
(S) (F)
4 RAKATS 4 RAKATS

MAGRIB
(F) (S) (N)
3 RAKATS 2 RAKATS 2 RAKATS

ISHA
(S) (F) (S) (N) (W) (N)
4 RAKATS 4 RAKATS 2 RAKATS 2 RAKATS 3 RAKATS 2 RAKATS

THOUGHTS & REFLECTIONS

- ☐ FASTED
- ☐ CHARITY
- ☐ ....
- ☐ ....

NIGHT 27

TARAWIH:
(2 RAKATS EACH)

(N) (N)
(N) (N)
(N) (N)
(N) (N)
(N) (N)

TAHAJJUD:
(2 RAKATS EACH)

(N) (N)
(N) (N)

REMINDERS:

1) ....
2) ....
3) ....
4) ....

DU'AS:

FOR THE NIGHT OF DESTINY

ALLAHUMMA INNAKA `AFUWWUN
TUHIBBUL `AFWA FA`FU `ANNEE
O ALLAH YOU ARE THE ONE WHO FORGIVES GREATLY,
AND LOVES TO FORGIVE, SO FORGIVE ME
IBN MAJAH: 3850, AT-TIRMIDHI: 3513

THERE EMERGES
FROM THEIR BELLIES A DRINK, VARYING IN COLOURS,
IN WHICH THERE IS HEALING FOR PEOPLE.
INDEED IN THAT IS A SIGN FOR A PEOPLE WHO GIVE THOUGHT.
16:69

BISMILLAH

DAY 27

…./…./….

FAJR
(S) (F)
2 RAKATS 2 RAKATS

DHUHR
(S) (F) (S) (N)
4 RAKATS 4 RAKATS 2 RAKATS 2 RAKATS

ASR
(S) (F)
4 RAKATS 4 RAKATS

MAGRIB
(F) (S) (N)
6 RAKATS 2 RAKATS 2 RAKATS

ISHA
(S) (F) (S) (N) (W) (N)
4 RAKATS 4 RAKATS 2 RAKATS 2 RAKATS 6 RAKATS 2 RAKATS

THOUGHTS & REFLECTIONS

☐ FASTED
☐ CHARITY
☐ ……………
☐ ……………

NIGHT 28
TARAWIH:
(2 RAKATS EACH)

(N) (N)
(N) (N)
(N) (N)
(N) (N)
(N) (N)

TAHAJJUD:
(2 RAKATS EACH)

REMINDERS:
1) …………………………………………
2) …………………………………………
3) …………………………………………
4) …………………………………………

DU'AS:

I SEEK REFUGE WITH ALLAH
AGAINST THE SATAN, THE OUTCAST.
ABU DAWUD: 4781 AL-BUKHARI: 6115

Subhan
ALLAHi
wa bihamdihi
Subhan
ALLAHiL
Azim

BISMILLAH

FAJR
(S) (F)
2 RAKATS 2 RAKATS

DHUHR
(S) (F) (S) (N)
4 RAKATS 4 RAKATS 2 RAKATS 2 RAKATS

ASR
(S) (F)
4 RAKATS 4 RAKATS

MAGRIB
(F) (S) (N)
6 RAKATS 2 RAKATS 2 RAKATS

ISHA
(S) (F) (S) (N) (W) (N)
4 RAKATS 4 RAKATS 2 RAKATS 2 RAKATS 6 RAKATS 2 RAKATS

DAY 28
.... / .... / ....

- [ ] FASTED
- [ ] CHARITY
- [ ] ....
- [ ] ....

NIGHT 29
TARAWIH:
(2 RAKATS EACH)

TAHAJJUD:
(2 RAKATS EACH)

THOUGHTS & REFLECTIONS

REMINDERS:
1) ....
2) ....
3) ....
4) ....

DU'AS:
O ALLAH, I SEEK REFUGE IN YOU
FROM GRIEF AND SADNESS,
FROM WEAKNESS AND FROM LAZINESS,
FROM MISERLINESS AND FROM COWARDICE,
FROM BEING OVERCOME BY DEBT
AND OVERPOWERED BY MEN (I.E. OTHERS).
AL-BUKHARI: 2893, 5425, 6363, 6369

WHEN LIFE
GIVES YOU
LEMONS...
JUST SAY
'ALHAMDULILLAH!'

BISMILLAH

DAY 29

..../..../....

FAJR
(S) (F)
2 RAKATS 2 RAKATS

DHUHR
(S) (F) (S) (N)
4 RAKATS 4 RAKATS 2 RAKATS 2 RAKATS

ASR
(S) (F)
4 RAKATS 4 RAKATS

MAGRIB
(F) (S) (N)
6 RAKATS 2 RAKATS 2 RAKATS

ISHA
(S) (F) (S) (N) (W) (N)
4 RAKATS 4 RAKATS 2 RAKATS 2 RAKATS 6 RAKATS 2 RAKATS

THOUGHTS & REFLECTIONS

☐ FASTED
☐ CHARITY
☐ ....
☐ ....

NIGHT 30
TARAWIH:
(2 RAKATS EACH)

(N) (N)
(N) (N)
(N) (N)
(N) (N)
(N) (N)

TAHAJJUD:
(2 RAKATS EACH)

(N) (N)
(N) (N)

REMINDERS:
1) ....
2) ....
3) ....
4) ....

DU'AS:
O ALLAH,
I ASK YOU FOR KNOWLEDGE
WHICH IS BENEFICIAL AND SUSTENANCE
WHICH IS GOOD,
AND DEEDS WHICH ARE ACCEPTABLE.
(TO BE SAID AFTER GIVING SALAM
FOR THE FAJR PRAYER)
IBN MAJAH 1:152

SO LET NOT
THIS PRESENT LIFE
DECEIVE YOU
35:5

BISMILLAH

DAY 30
..../..../....

FAJR

(S) (F)
2 RAKATS 2 RAKATS

DHUHR

(S) (F) (S) (N)
4 RAKATS 4 RAKATS 2 RAKATS 2 RAKATS

ASR

(S) (F)
4 RAKATS 4 RAKATS

MAGRIB

(F) (S) (N)
6 RAKATS 2 RAKATS 2 RAKATS

ISHA

(S) (F) (S) (N) (W) (N)
4 RAKATS 4 RAKATS 2 RAKATS 2 RAKATS 6 RAKATS 2 RAKATS

THOUGHTS & REFLECTIONS

☐ FASTED
☐ CHARITY
☐ ....
☐ ....

NIGHT 31

EID
MUBARAK!

REMINDERS:
1) ....
2) ....
3) ....
4) ....

DU'AS:
OH ALLAH,
ACCEPT MY EFFORTS DURING THIS MONTH,
ALL OF MY PRAYERS AND FASTS,
AND ALLOW THEM TO WEIGH HEAVILY
ON THE SCALES OF GOOD.

Printed in Great Britain
by Amazon

38415818R00039

ISBN 9798706169756

90000

9 798706 169756